Hello!

I'm Creative Florence, Flo for shor
I am an Illustrator & Designer anc
the road from David.

I love working with coloured tissue paper to create
images with lots of texture!

Then I make digital pictures to create books like this one!
Together, we have created a book of wonderful words and
images for Christmas.

We would love to know what your favourite poem and
illustration is.

Get in touch and let us know!

x

Hello I'm Finny

Creative Helper

December 1st

One day, I'll be a "grown-up", but that is not today
Today, I'm just a "kid" and that is great
Because....   Wa-hey!
It's Day 1 on the Advent. That means I get a treat!
A special door to open? With surprise inside?
That's sweet!

I'm not sure what a "Grown-Up" is
Does it just mean your size?
Or are you given knowledge at an age?
Some rules and guides?

My Grown-Ups are quite funny
So that is a relief
I'm just a kid, but funny things are good
That's my belief
I always want to laugh a lot, whatever time of year
So I will try to make them laugh
Now Christmas is quite near

Just 23 more advent doors, or 23 more sleeps
I'll make a funny Christmas card
At school. That they can keep
I'll draw a goofy face on Santa
Make some reindeer poo
Make the Elves pull faces
Cos I think that's what 'kids' do

I think you keep these cards, right?
And put them in a box?
Then store them in the loft-space
Beside the Christmas socks?

I see them when you get the tree
When lists and cards are done
When all the "Christmas Jobs" begin
Before the "Christmas Fun"

This time of year, you grown-ups rush
Your minds are in a muddle
I hope you know that all I "want"?
Is love.   Your time.   A cuddle

Dreamy Tortoise

I may not be the fastest tortoise, or the swiftest round the room
But that is just an oxymoron. Think I'm daft? You thought too soon
My brain is full of information. All the facts that I have heard
For I have time for contemplation. I remember every word

And what's the benefit of this? Well, I heard once that dreams are thoughts
The bits left over when night the falls. Assorted scraps to play, cavort
I should explain, my use of language sometimes brings a bouncy phrase
For "bouncing" otherwise is tricky. When your heavy shell delays

What worries me? A thing that's caused me consternation more than once?
The young folk call it hibernation. Happy time! (I dream, for months)
But this year, (why, I do not know!) The young folk? They've gone 'Google' mad
And this now means my food has stopped. They've bought a fridge
And thermal pad (?!)

Apparently, I need to starve. "To flush out toxins and hydrate"
They're bathing me, providing drinks. To force a prompt to "defecate"
When I get snoozy they will pounce, and put me in an ice-cream tub
Place holes in lid, into the fridge. A thermostatic tortoise hub

The fridge will be at 5 degrees. They'll weigh me weekly. Check my health
Whatever happened to a box? Some hay, an airing cupboard shelf?
But now I think, the airing cupboard went this year. New bathroom done
So maybe that's their only choice? To make me dream of snowy fun?

Maybe I need to move, adapt. For I'll be here for many years
And yearning for the days gone by, can often simply grind the gears
So I will dream of sledging, whizzing down a mountain on my shell
Of meeting Santa, snowmen too, dream tales that only sleep can tell

Silly Songs

A class can be bouncy at this time of year
So the teachers devised a fine plan
They let the kids go, let them right off the leash
Said "Re-write Christmas songs"
They began...

"Away in a manger, with a bib on his head
The Little Lord Jesus found the new chocolate spread
The Mars Bars all had bites, why?
He'd looked round and thought: "Yay!
I don't like baby cheeses, at the end of the day"

They liked the re-working. The tune just jumped out
And the kid was a big chocolate fan
And next up was Susie. A true science buff
She would educate. That was her plan...

"Jingle Bells, red blood cells, carbon dioxide
Haemoglobin, air is thrown in, then you breathe away, hey!
Jingle bells, red blood cells, take bad gas away
They transport your oxygen on the long course of your day"

This one was a curve-ball in all honesty
The gas-exchange properties of blood
But they'd said to re-write, to create and be free
And next up? Was wonderful Judd

"Rudolph the red-nosed reindeer
painted very shiny toes
And if you ever saw them
You'd think he belonged in shows

Called up his brother's trained ear
On behalf of his new aims
But X-Factor ditched poor Rudolph
Now he's back behind the reins"

The teacher was rocked by this tragic, sad tale
A character everyone knew
Trying to break out of a stereotype
Then crushed by a mean TV crew

But giving the children a blank page to fill
Had opened up doors in their mind
They'd written from truths in their lives that they liked
A lesson so precious to find

Chocolate plans

I think this year (unlike the others when there's been no structure)
I'll make a chocolate rota, so my tummy knows the score
Cos let's be honest, Christmas means you eat until you rupture
So if I make a road-map? I can pace it. Then eat more!

The first ones? Well, it has to be. The coins inside my stocking
And technically they're chocolate but the taste is never great
So I'll just dabble, one or two, cos then I will be knocking
The Terry's Orange on the floor. It's Christmas, so why wait?

The orange tang? Like toothpaste, kind of. Breakfast mouth is fresh
Some scrambled egg, some toast, some juice. The healthy stuff? All done
And then it's to the lounge for presents. Big unwrapping sesh
And on the side? The Roses tub. It's opened. Bring the fun

I've learned well, over many years, that no-one likes the coffees
So if you bide your time and wait, your route is pretty clear
For when the others lock their jaws with caramels and toffees
I swoop in, hoover up the lot. No challenge and no fear

The only downside? Furry teeth. And "savoury" tastes wrong
The remedy? Well. It's one day. Embrace it. Fight the cause
The only thing that you can do? Keep chomping, Carry on
For soon the Christmas Dinner will provide a chocky pause

Until that is, when plates are cleared, the cheeses, grapes and dates
The cracker pulled, my tummy full. So bloated that I yawn
Then some bright spark unwraps the big green box of After Eights
I fondle many wrappers. Battle-lines are now redrawn

You know what? As I'm planning this, remembering my past
This yearly Christmas excess, that is making me feel ill?
Maybe it's time to reassess. To have one. Make it last
It makes sense now, but still, somehow, I know I never will

Book list

There's something I love. It's the smell of a book
The cover, with pictures all saying "Just look!"
I quite like a series, a character or theme
Or sometimes, I just like a weird, crazy dream

So maybe this year I will write a big list
And leave it out somewhere, so it can't be missed
Cos there are a few that I just want to hold
To read them, to hear them, to feel pages fold

Or maybe I'll weave the list into these lines
Cos when I write rhymes, mum says that her heart shines
So can I have "Penguin" by Polly Dunbar, please?
And "The Imaginary" or "The Afterwards" by AF Harrold?
Oh, FREEZE!

I need all the "Oi" books. I think Jim Field's ace!
And "The Lion Inside". Rachel Bright's rhymes have pace
Could I have Rachel Rooney: "A Kid in My Class"?
And "Hey, Girl" or "My Life as a Goldfish" would pass!

I suppose that's enough, for now. I will just see
If all, or just some of these books come to me
One day, I would love to draw things for a living
Bring somebody's words to life. Ready for giving

For now though? I'll just keep on twirling my pens
Read books, find new stories and share them with friends
This world can be tough. Yes, whatever your age is
But I'm always safe, amongst drawings and pages

Elves

If Elves fill the shelves up for Santa
Make presents and big gifts appear
Work hard in November.
Harder still in December
What happens the rest of the year?

Do Santa's Elves tend to the reindeer?
Plant carrots for Rudolph to eat?
Do they fix the sleigh?
Dents picked up on the way
Ironed out, so it's shiny and neat?

Do Elves do the paper recycling?
The lists sent to Santa each year
Cards sent to "North Pole". Read, ticked off as a whole
Then pulped, so new lists can appear?

Or maybe Elves have magic habits?
To recharge their batteries for work?
Asleep for three seasons, then wake for good reasons
As the toy sheds and tasks go berserk?

Or are they employed on a contract?
With uniquely weird work conditions?
Ten months off, two on, until Santa is gone
On his worldwide and magical missions?

If I was an Elf, I'd be happy
I'd like to live at the North Pole
Watch polar bears, walrus and
Northern Lights' chorus
With friends in a scraped, snowy hole

I guess we will never know, really
And maybe that's fine. We can dream
But if you read this, why not make
your own list
Tell your grown-ups
about your Elf Team

Acrostic Poetry Is Weird

Poetry today, my class! We're going to write acrostic verse!"

Oh great. What does **that** word mean? (this day is going bad to worse)

Everyone should know a poem's meant to rhyme on every line

Theme of Christmas? Timing, pace, imagination? That's all fine

Really though, a poem with no rhyming? Miss? Are you quite sure?

Yes you say. Just write your truth. Free up the things that rhymes obscure

I think Miss has stayed up late. She isn't making any sense

So here is my acrostic verse. My Christmas, rhyming self-defence

When Christmas comes, it gets quite cold. But never snowy, like the books

Evening eating sandwiches. It's just leftovers. No-one cooks

Ice cream's yum but only ever served with yucky Christmas pud

Really Pudding? Set on fire? As grown-ups cheer, like that is good?

Don't like poems. What's acrostic? Now this rhythm's lost the plot

(Dot Dot dot-dot Dot Dot dot-dot Dot Dot dot-dot dot-dot Dot)

Space Pen

My mum has got a Space Pen
So she can write in space
She told me she's an astronaut
But never leaves a trace

Each night when Mummy tucks me in
She reads a book, or three
Gives Ted a hug, then me a kiss
But then, apparently...

She goes into the garage
When I have gone to sleep
Then puts her spacesuit on... Flies off
With Zoom! And Roar! And Leap!

The spaceship is a secret
She says it's in her mind
But if my mind can picture it?
It might be mine to find

It might be there to fly me off
To places no-one's been
To find new lands and aliens
That we have never seen

To make new friends, to wave and smile
Find stories to be told
To celebrate the youngest minds
And honour all the old

I don't think Mum's an astronaut
She's got a dodgy knee
She wears big, black-framed glasses
And often needs a wee

But every night, she holds her pen
She travels many miles
She writes me many stories
And she brings back many smiles

Helping out

This year. We're "Going to be doing our bit"
That's what mum and her boyfriend say
We're all going to help at the big local hall
Help others to have Christmas Day

I think that I like the idea, if I'm honest
It feels like a good thing to do
It might feel quite weird when we get there
But that's what it's like when it's new

We'll likely see all sorts of people and ages
Hear all types of languages too
I hope I can make just one stranger's day better
Or give them a hug, if they're blue

And really, the more that I think of it
The more it just seems to make sense
We don't have a lot either, but we can help
A small thought. But, maybe, immense

Myrrh

Because I'm in Year 6, there's things I really need to know
And sometimes I just wonder why I think these things alone?
We'll soon do our Nativity. The annual Christmas show
And in it, just like every year, we'll see things so well known

The little ones will shuffle in, with tea-towels on their head
The parents will then gasp and smile with "oohs" and "ahhs" and sniffs
And then they'll wind their way to baby Jesus in his bed
Before just standing, waiting, for Three Kings with special gifts

And this is where my brain lights up. With questions never solved
Cos everybody knows the things the Three Wise Men will bring
However bad the props. It's myrrh and frankincense and gold
And they will set the gifts down at the cradle of the king

And that's all fine. But hiding in plain sight? Two random words
I'm Year 6 now and no-one's ever told me what they were
And yes, I could just Google it, or ask the swots and nerds
But what, pray tell, is frankincense? And what on earth is myrrh?

It's like they were included to flush out the wise or brave
Two items no-one's heard of (except now, at Christmas time)
So if I pose the question, I don't mean to misbehave
Can someone say what myrrh is, please? I'm open, here. I'm primed

Fly rhythms shyly. Dry wry pygmy. Sentences. No vowel
But myrrh is on its own. It never looks right on the page
But this year? I'm Year 6. And I will not throw in the towel
And Frankincense? In my defence. I might just have a gauge

The word sounds pretty. Smelly too? Like something you would want
The props for this one sometimes are a box with jewels and beads
But have I ever seen it in a church or at a font?
I haven't, no. The box for show? If fooling? It succeeds

So when I leave Year 6 and I'm allowed to get a phone
(my olds have promised, so I'll get connected to my peers)
The first thing that I Google? (in a safe place, on my own)
I'll type in Frankincense and Myrrh. So years of fog then clears

But if you're reading this aloud. And someone is nearby
I dare you. I implore you. Life's too short. We need to grow
When you have finished reading, just look up and catch their eye
Then calmly ask.: "I have a task. Here's what I'd like to know..."

Foxy Bandit

Somewhere, near me, a special Christmas Tree is taking shape
The image that just popped up in your head? Well, scrap that now
For this one doesn't stand. It's just some branches in a scrape
But every day it has new decorations. And here's how

The maker of the tree? A local legend: Foxy Bandit
An orange flash at dusk. A silent shadow in the night
We don't know if he thought it or he ever could have planned it
And some say that his decorations? Well, they're just not right

No angel. But there is a soggy, one-eyed, chewed up teddy
No tinsel (but the bras from washing-lines make up for that)
No baubles. Just some quick-nabbed toys and tea-towels, placed and ready
For Foxy Bandit steals and raids. He rules his habitat

But do not, for one second, think that Foxy's wise or regal
He's chosen an appearance that wipes out all sense of style
His trademark 'look'? The pants he took. Illicit and illegal
They're blue and white and stripy. You can spot him from a mile

The owner of the pants was Flo, whose drawings fill this book
She's trying to find the funny side. As Foxy gets more famous
But maybe we should ponder. Take a longer second look
Not at the pants. That's wrong. At why young Foxy entertains us

A part of me believes, or hopes, that Foxy cares a lot
He's practising philanthropy. To help make others smile
So when he wears Flo's pants? The foxes pooing in a pot?
Might just adjust their actions. Find a poo place more worthwhile

And as his name is shared and others start to hear and follow
He takes responsibility for leading his new flock
His stealing? Maybe just revealing, in his branch-filled hollow
A safe place they can congregate, or bring a soggy sock

Because, regardless if we're urban (humans or a fox)
There's something that all mammals need. All mammals need to share
It's something to believe in. Precious, caring building blocks
So here's to Foxy Bandit. And his Christmas Tree of care

Christmas Crackers

You hold a cracker once each year
And that is why it's special
You know you'll hear an awful joke
You'll have a jokey wrestle

You'll all put paper hats on, too
The treats go on the floor
They fall out of a loo-roll, really
So, what are crackers for?

That's easy, I can tell you
A cracker is 'tradition'
That's what the grown-ups say
As they set off upon their mission

To flip frogs into trifle
To spin the top for hours
To find the fortune-teller fish
And marvel at its powers

To wind up toys and race them
Solve puzzles. Prove they're clever
To laugh at truly awful jokes
But always laugh, together

I think that's what a cracker's for
A thing to hold and share
A crack, a smile. The '"wins"? Worthwhile
Because they mean you're 'there'

Just right there, in the present
A moment to connect
To let go. Find the fun again
These things? We should protect

Nana

This Christmas is different. There's something not right
A gap, which has just never been there before
I'm trying to picture this year. Christmas night
Then Boxing Day visits. The routine. The law

This Christmas is different. My Nana has gone
We had to say bye in the Summer this year
That day was warm. Now it's cold. It feels wrong
It's hard to believe that she cannot be here

My Nana loved Christmas. She made the best cakes
She knitted us hats, gave us jams and a cuddle
If I think about her, my chest kind of aches
I don't feel excited. My mind is a muddle

I tell Mum and Dad. They say "Leave it to us"
"We know you feel sad, but we're making a plan"
I know they'll do something, without a big fuss
I trust them. They get it. They both understand

And then today Mum taps her glass at the table
Says: "Family? We all need a quick Christmas talk"
"This year will be different. But some things are stable
This year, Grandad's joining our Boxing Day walk"

They're picking him up Christmas Eve, from his home
He's bringing the sweets Christmas visits provide
He's going to be here, so he won't be alone
And then Dad says this. His eyes wet with a shine:

"We're setting a place at the table for both
For Nana and Grandad. Because, let's be clear
She's still in our heart, so we'll smile
Say this oath:
"We can't see you, but we all know
You are here"

Christmas Time Birthday

To all of you big grown-ups out there?
A message that comes from the heart
And hopefully, once you have heard it?
You'll realise what sets me apart

It soon will be Christmas. That's lovely
But please, try to show some respect
My birthday? You guessed it:
At "Christmas Time" Meh
And this year, I need to object

I've waited some years for this moment
And most of them? I've had short shrift
But this year. Please hear this (quite loudly):

I DON'T WANT A "NICE, COMBINED GIFT"!

My birthday is not of my choosing
(It may not have been dad and mum's)
Aaaaand ... I don't want to think of that really
Them snogging, 9 months and the sums

But "Christmas Time" birthdays are rubbish!
I don't even get my own cake!
They take Santa off, grab a candle
Don't try to disguise it's a fake!

If I had been born in September?
I'd have my own birthday. A day
"Birthday weekend"? Aaaagh! You're so lucky!
That's it... I must fix this some way

I'm going to have a "Half-Birthday"
A date in June, all just for **ME!**
No gifts to condense
My own party and presents
No Santa or turkey or tree!

See It and Be It

This Christmas? This year? I feel different and proud
And now, some days? I want to shout that out loud!
Because before summer, my 'difference' was mine
A silent thing. Others would look. That was fine

It wasn't fine, really. It's never been that
But I get it. Some folk don't know how to act
When I'm wheeling, I have control of my chair
It's just how I move, but some people still stare

And some days I deal with misguided assumptions
When I meet new people who see how I function
My legs are not great mate but, please, don't ignore me!
Or talk slow and loud, finish sentences for me!

I deal with a thing that is called disability
But this year? I've seen I can smash its fragility
Prove people's perceptions of what can be done
By "someone like me"? They're just wrong. It's begun

I've seen wheelchair racers. The Commonwealth Games
A Gold, Silver, Bronze. Athletes reaching their aims
The medals, a badge that says "Watch us and dream"
Then find a club, train. One day? Hear **your** crowds scream!

They say: "If you don't see it? Then you can't be it"
Well, I've seen it now. I have power. I must free it
I've seen those three athletes. The best in their field
A stadium roaring. Not shy. Not concealed

A true celebration of what wheels can give
To race for your nation, then share what you live
For all of those athletes had stories to share
I'm starting my story. And one day?

I'll be there

Bun's Miracle

The trip started sideways. Wedged space on the bus
Mum checked her list again. Dad "surfed" and smiled
A stop, bump and spin. Then for Joe? Noise and fuss
His buggy rolled, bags whizzing by, fast and wild

His Mum had a list, Dad had written one, too
Both started apps, just for fun, for their routes
And now, they were off! Many gifts to get through
For Joe, this now meant a quick trundle to Boots

Then? Doomph. A new rhythm. Bag hooked on the handle
Now every footstep produced a new beat
Joe smiled and looked down at his mum's comfy sandal
She walked and it thumped with each step of her feet

And as Joe looked out, he showed "Bun" the view, too
His favourite soft thing. He waved it with joy
Bun's long ears flapped swiftly. But then, as Bun flew?
He dropped from the hand of the small, happy boy

The sound of the street and the buses and bustle
Meant even though Joe called out loud in despair
His mum couldn't hear him. Bun fell into hustle
Joined wrappers and flyers and lost bands for hair

Much later, Joe's parents met, as they had planned
They kissed, looked at Joe and then saw he looked sad
So, out of the buggy, to soothe, understand
Then a reach down for Bun. The best thing for their lad

And there, in that moment, three hearts became one
New plans were made quickly to retread their routes
They'd finish their lists but they'd look out for Bun
But after a while they both had heavy boots

They had to make tracks to the bus stop. Get home
So then, with a stone heavy footstep, they walked
They all were together. But felt so alone
They looked all around, up and down, hardly talked

Joe was now sleeping. His head on mum's shoulder
Dreaming of Bun. In the noise of the street
The darkness was draping them, air getting colder
No spring in the step now. Just shuffling feet

But sometimes, whatever your truths or beliefs
Small miracles happen. For those that are good
And suddenly, giving true joy and relief
His parents both gasped. Looked at where Santa stood

A Santa who'd helped at a food bank in town
And now was preparing to catch the same bus
A Santa who paused near the stop, looked around
And placed a small Bun on the wall without fuss

He'd already written a sign on some card
It said: "Found today. Share me. Let's cast a spell"
For this Santa knew viral shares were not hard
He hoped he could help a good story to tell

And as he turned round, he saw two parents gasping
One held a child in their arms, now awake
His eyes open wide, smiling, beaming and grasping
A reach out for Bun. His dad's arm in a shake

They sat on the bus. Rode the way home together
They found out this Santa knew no-one. Was new
So that year, in very rare, cold, snowy weather
That Santa? Spent Christmas with Joe, and Bun too

The Twelve Parps of Christmas

It's the first parp of Christmas. Post-dinner, cup of tea
A parp squidged from dinner scares me

It's the second parp of Christmas, and it's a mystery
Phew, someone does and a parp squidged from dinner scares me

It's the third parp of Christmas. It's mummy, I can see
Scents mum sends, Phew, someone does and
a parp squidged from dinner scares me

It's the fourth parp of Christmas, I think that one was me
Think no-one heard, scents mum sends, Phew, someone does
and a parp squidged from dinner scares me

It's the fifth parp of Christmas. Though this one I can't see
Wow! That one SINGS! Think no-one heard, scents mum sends,
Phew, someone does and a parp squidged from dinner scares me

It's the sixth parp of Christmas, dad's sloped off for a wee
"Decrease", I'm praying. Wow! That one SINGS! Think no-one
heard, scents mum sends, Phew, someone does
and a parp squidged from dinner scares me

It's the seventh parp of Christmas, just picture and agree
Our lounge is brimming, "Decrease", I'm praying
Wow! That one SINGS! Think no-one heard, scents mum
sends, Phew, someone does and a parp squidged from dinner scares me

It's the eighth parp of Christmas, I'm trying to smell the tree
Its leaves are wilting, our lounge is brimming, "Decrease",
I'm praying. Wow! That one SINGS! Think no-one heard,
scents mum sends, Phew, someone does and a parp squidged
from dinner scares me

It's the ninth parp of Christmas, It's fuggy, rescue me!
Hades advancing, tree leaves are wilting,
our lounge is brimming, "Decrease", I'm praying
Wow! That one SINGS! Think no-one heard,
scents mum sends, Phew, someone does
and a parp squidged from dinner scares me

It's the tenth parp of Christmas, excuses all round me
"Floorboards are creaking", Hades advancing, tree leaves
are wilting, our lounge is brimming, "Decrease", I'm praying
Wow! That one SINGS! Think no-one heard, scents mum
sends, Phew, someone does and a parp squidged from dinner scares me

It's the eleventh parp of Christmas, it's getting hard to see
My eyes I'm wiping, "Floorboards are creaking",
Hades advancing, tree leaves are wilting, our lounge
is brimming, "Decrease", I'm praying
Wow! That one SINGS!
Think no-one heard, scents mum sends,
Phew, someone does and a parp squidged from dinner scares me

It's the twelfth parp of Christmas, and surely it must mean
Our plumber's coming, my eyes I'm wiping,
"Floorboards are creaking" Hades advancing,
tree leaves are wilting, our lounge is brimming
"Decrease", I'm praying
Wow! That one SINGS!
Think no-one heard, scents mum sends,
Phew, someone does and a parp squidged from dinner   scares   me!

Bubble and Squeak

So there is this thing called "Tradition"
My parents? They love it. For sure
Because every year it's the word that I hear
As we stack pots and bags at the door

One bag? The left-over crackers
One bag? The cold Christmas pud
One bag? Some port, smelly cheeses cut short
After yesterday's meal. Yum. All good

Let's face it. It's leftovers, really
Just taken to grandparent's houses
But when we arrive, the whole place comes alive
With "tradition" our bag just arouses

My grandad is holding the masher
My Nana? Her knees have gone weak
The spuds? On the bubble. And soon, with no trouble
We'll tuck in to bubble and squeak

It's Brussels sprouts. Leftover, cold ones
Mixed in with mashed spuds and then fried
And sometimes the veg, claimed back with a knife-edge
From the plates Christmas Dinner supplied

We're gathered for "leftovers" dinner
That's what is it, really. Agreed?
You call it "Tradition".
But here's my admission...
It tastes very yummy indeed!

Our Caretaker is Father Christmas

Some things are just too exciting
And so, here's a thing I must share
I think our school caretaker **is** Father Christmas
Cos when Christmas comes? He's not there

And yes, no-one knows the real Santa
And our caretaker? He has no beard
But every December he "forgets to shave"
And then this white beard just appears

He always comes back with a haircut
His white, curly hair trimmed and neat
His chin a big grin with no beard there at all
And new shiny boots on his feet

His boots are those black ones, like Santa's
His favourite colour? It's red
And he likes to go where there's ice and there's snow
He has a big sled in his shed

We know this because he tells stories
Tells tales as he sweeps and repairs
There's a glint in his eye and I think I know why
So, I want to catch him unawares

I'll ask mum and dad for a present this year
To "Adopt a Reindeer" some place
I'll bring the certificate back into school
And then watch the look on his face

Cos reindeer came into our school once before
And he rang in. Said deer make him 'sick'
"Comes out in a rash". But I think that is trash
They'd just know our caretaker's Saint Nick

My big sister says that I'm silly
Believing in all of this stuff
But I know our caretaker **is** Father Christmas
And sometimes? Believing's enough

Christmas Socks

Mum and dad were chatting with their friends. All sat downstairs
I was in my room, it seemed the ideal place to be
But then I overheard them, listened. Caught them unawares
And some of what they said? Contained strange language. Well, to me

"Mum? So, what are paper-chains?" I said. And there was more
"And you just said 'Lametta'? I have never heard that word!"
"A Christmas Sock? Why not a Christmas sack? What were they for?!"
Fair play to mum (and dad). They took me back to their old world

Paper chains, they said, were like an old-school thing to make
A decoration draped from ceilings, going side to side
A corner start then wrap around the light. Sometimes they'd break
You had to lick bad glue, then wait, until the bad glue dried

Apparently, they came in packs. Like stacks of paper strips
But the different colours were the thing that made them fun
I found some later in my room. On grainy YouTube clips
My interest in grown-ups' Christmas past has now begun

Apparently Lametta was like tinsel, but more lame
Long tinsel. But in single bits. That tangled in your clothes
They spoke of it with reverence. It really staked a claim
In childhood memories. Well, for them. And why? Well, no-one knows
The last one? Melts my brain. I know my parents are quite old
But when were Christmas socks a thing? Were they the only ones?
They used to call them "stockings", too. That's what I have been told
If they just used a sock, then how could Santa have his fun?

They said they'd get an apple, nuts and sometimes a satsuma
But surely that would take up nearly all the room inside?
And then they said (I don't know if it's just their sense of humour)
The scrunch of paper through the sock, made little eyes go wide

A night-time fumble on the bed and then the call "He's Beeen!"
When sock and paper-scrunch was heard, then Christmas had arrived
And even when they told me? Biggest smiles that I have seen
My thoughts were wrong, I guess. Their life was simple. Not deprived

So this year, I'll be making paper-chains with mum and dad
And yes, they do not know it yet, but Etsy has some stocks
I'm going to find Lametta too. Good memories? Can't be bad
And this year? Night-time? Christmas Eve? I'll bring them...

Christmas Socks

Comparisons

My mate will get a PS5 this year
His birthday was last month
He got a new Nintendo Switch

I hope that some new Lego will appear
My mum likes eBay hunts
She says "Not all of us are rich"

And yes, I'd like a PS5 one day
(But maybe in four years
When PS6 will make them cheap)

With Lego? I just need a space to play
Some blocks and wheels and gears
If mum gets that? That's my clean sweep

I want to tell her really that it's fine
I don't need lots of 'stuff'
I know she sometimes feels alone

If Christmas is just us two?
Well, she's mine
And that much is enough
If we're together? That is home

X

Christmas Haiku

What is a Haiku?
The word sounds a bit funny
It's making me think

Sounds like a greeting
Although, who could be called "Ku"?
Maybe that's not it

I like the word, though
It sounds all bright and shiny
Like Christmas baubles

Like our new Tree lights
They sparkle, then do routines
I like the "pulse" best

Like the tree's happy
Excited. Counting down days
Its heartbeat. Rising

A quiet secret
That maybe only I know
But maybe that's me

I spot the patterns
I look for things others don't
My grown-ups say this

"Imagination
Might just be the greatest gift
We can hope to share"

Well, I'm just a kid
And though that sounds quite fancy?
My heart? Likes the sound

Spoken-word Christmas poem

At school, my teacher told me to write a poem about Christmas

I said: "Miss? It's like this, you see, I'll try to fit in with the plan, but please, I hope you can understand, my mind works differently"

I find that words have a natural bounce and a rhythm and my mind gives them an order to land on the page, or I store them in my head

Sometimes, in bed, I re-run chats I've had with the cat, when I try to freestyle as she's sat on my lap and she purrs, as my mind whirrs and it's already linking the next rhyme to the word that I'm thinking of and playing with

Staying with a theme, then diverting into different routes, seeing where the natural rhythm and the pattern shoots me off to play

My mind works like this. Every.   Single.   Day.

Is it a gift? I don't know. Does it give me a lift? Yes. Cos sometimes, you know, it's hard to start a conversation when the subject matter is tricky, if you know it could get sticky or your words might not come out right, you fight to get your point across in your mind as you plan it, then you find the moment's gone and you haven't landed anything of note

So I freestyle and let my mind go where it needs to go for a while

So Christmas? To me? It's watching the Snowman float above the snow, soft hand in hand with the boy who planned to bring him into the world. Scenes unfurled in front of my eyes as they move through skies that everyone else ignores and just takes for granted

The unchanted, unspoken dreams of a kid, rising above the hustle and bustle of Christmas. No wish-list ticked off, just pure, joyous lift-off, and escape

So, I'll try to make a poem about Christmas. I'll try to fit a pattern, bounce along and make a verse. I'll try to adhere to the structure that the lesson-plan infers. But if I can't fit the expected pattern? If I can't produce twelve lines that fit and rhyme? If it doesn't happen?

Miss? At least I've been honest with you.
And I hope. Really hope.
That'll do

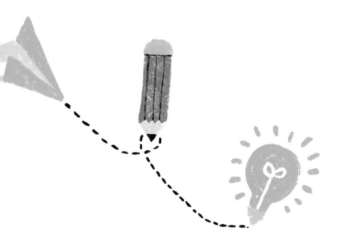

Christmas Eve

It may just be the most exciting day of all the year
The one before your birthday? Good. But never quite the same
So let's all think about it. Because soon, it will be near
This day is just so special that it's given its own name

What will you do this Christmas Eve? The things you always do?
The Snowman, Elf or Father Christmas played on your TV?
And in the evening will you find pyjamas. Wrapped and new?
If you leave things for Rudolph on a plate. What will they be?

Do you leave carrots? Mince pies? Drinks? Where do you put the plate?
And will you look through windows, just in case you see a sleigh?
Will grown-ups go to church. Sing hymns? Feel warmth they can create?
Will stockings be hung up? Or left on beds for Christmas Day?

Or maybe this year could be one when something new is done
A way to celebrate at Christmas you've not tried before
In Iceland? Every Christmas Eve. New books, for everyone
Wrapped up then handed over, with hot chocolate, for fun

A way to calm the mind, relax and curl up with a tale
To turn off all the noise and drift away into new worlds
The simple things? We find them, hold them, for they never fail
If you are in a book? You're safe. Away from bumps and swirls

So this year, Christmas Eve could be the one you try new things
Deliver food, sing songs to people, help a friend or two
Find joy in just the simple fun that time together brings
And as a last suggestion, why not try this one out, too?

Just list the happy, brave or good things you have done this year
A little Christmas re-cap as your year comes to an end
Next year on Christmas Eve? Re-read them. Good things will appear
Reminders how much you are growing. Safely stored and penned

And if you start this year, who knows? In many years from now?
You'll have a big collection of your fears and hopes and dreams
A record of your progress. How you beat the odds somehow
Say: "Christmas Eve is magical. And I am too, it seems..."

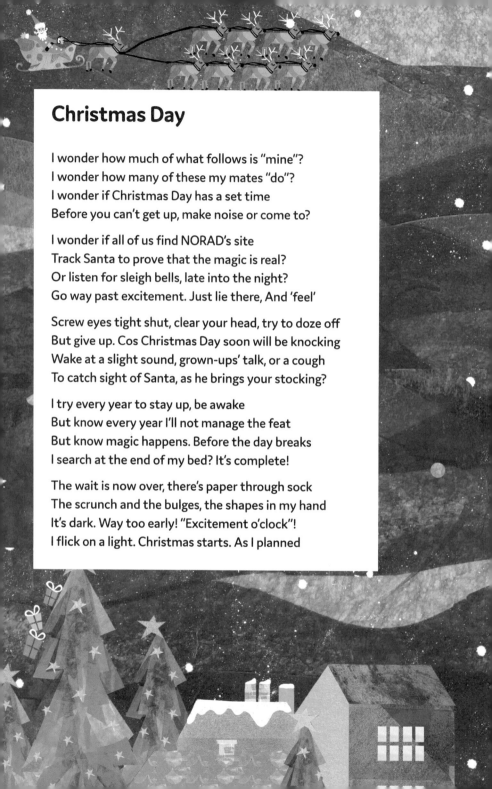

Christmas Day

I wonder how much of what follows is "mine"?
I wonder how many of these my mates "do"?
I wonder if Christmas Day has a set time
Before you can't get up, make noise or come to?

I wonder if all of us find NORAD's site
Track Santa to prove that the magic is real?
Or listen for sleigh bells, late into the night?
Go way past excitement. Just lie there, And 'feel'

Screw eyes tight shut, clear your head, try to doze off
But give up. Cos Christmas Day soon will be knocking
Wake at a slight sound, grown-ups' talk, or a cough
To catch sight of Santa, as he brings your stocking?

I try every year to stay up, be awake
But know every year I'll not manage the feat
But know magic happens. Before the day breaks
I search at the end of my bed? It's complete!

The wait is now over, there's paper through sock
The scrunch and the bulges, the shapes in my hand
It's dark. Way too early! "Excitement o'clock"!
I flick on a light. Christmas starts. As I planned

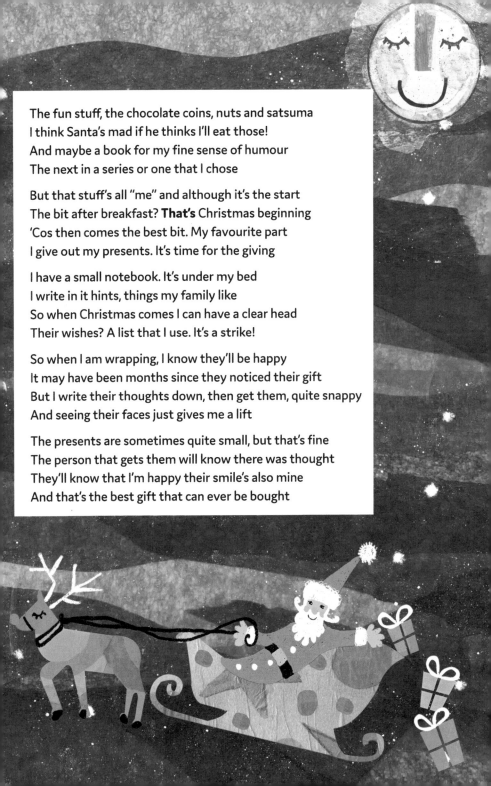

The fun stuff, the chocolate coins, nuts and satsuma
I think Santa's mad if he thinks I'll eat those!
And maybe a book for my fine sense of humour
The next in a series or one that I chose

But that stuff's all "me" and although it's the start
The bit after breakfast? **That's** Christmas beginning
'Cos then comes the best bit. My favourite part
I give out my presents. It's time for the giving

I have a small notebook. It's under my bed
I write in it hints, things my family like
So when Christmas comes I can have a clear head
Their wishes? A list that I use. It's a strike!

So when I am wrapping, I know they'll be happy
It may have been months since they noticed their gift
But I write their thoughts down, then get them, quite snappy
And seeing their faces just gives me a lift

The presents are sometimes quite small, but that's fine
The person that gets them will know there was thought
They'll know that I'm happy their smile's also mine
And that's the best gift that can ever be bought

Boxing Day

Boxing Day is precious
The pressure-valve of Christmas Day is done
It is a day to let off steam

To bundle gifts, put clinky-clanky bags in the boot
Put your furry, floppy Santa hats on

One more time, so you can wave at strangers

Then drive

To a hug
To smiles
To what you already know you are going to do

Warm greetings and cold meats
With salad instead of spuds because, well,
It's nearly New Years Resolution time, right?

And then?
Time to talk
Strava and Apps quietly recording
Your happy walk in the woods

But when you stop, look up at the birds
Find shapes in the clouds?

The silence of it all

A small branch crack and snap underfoot
Punctuating a relaxed chat

And then back
To a sandwich and the last of the 'big bag' of crisps
To cups of tea and spicy, boozy, almondy
Icing-topped cake with, if you're lucky
A glacé cherry in your slice. Very nice

January can wait
For today is Boxing Day
The rest day of Christmas
The best day of Christmas